PRIMARY WORD WORK

Introductory Book

Louis Fidge
Sarah Lindsay

Collins Educational

An imprint of HarperCollins*Publishers*

Published by Collins Educational
An imprint of HarperCollinsPublishers Ltd
77-85 Fulham Palace Road
London W6 8JB

© Louis Fidge and Sarah Lindsay 1998

First published 1998
Reprinted 2001

ISBN 0 00 302485 7

Louis Fidge and Sarah Lindsay assert the moral right to be identified as the authors of this work.

Illustrations by Maggie Brand, Rob Englebright, Belinda Evans, Bethan Matthews, Andrew Midgley, Lisa Smith

British Library Cataloguing in Publication Data
A catalogue record for this book is available from the British Library.

Cover illustration: Rob Englebright
Editor: Janet Swarbrick
Designer: Celia Hart

Contents

UNIT 1 — oo and u

The letters **oo** and **u** often make the same **sound**.

b**oo**k

b**u**ll

Practice

Copy the words.

Circle the u words. Underline the oo words.

1.

(pulley)

2.

cook

3.

hook

4.

bull

5.

wood

6.

bully

More to think about

Copy the table. Write the words in the correct columns.

oo	u
book	

hook

hood

cook

full

pull

wood

book   bull

Now try these

1. Copy the sentences. Choose the correct word.
   a) The jar is (fool/full) of sweets.
   b) Peter works as a (book/cook) in a big kitchen.
   c) The chair is made out of (good/wood).
   d) Sam didn't let the (bully/fully) frighten her.

2. Make up a sentence for each word.
   a) bull   b) good   c) pull

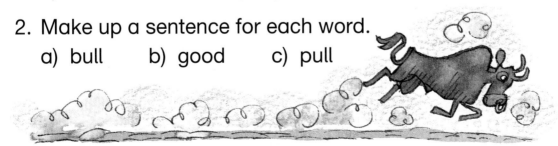

Collecting words (1)

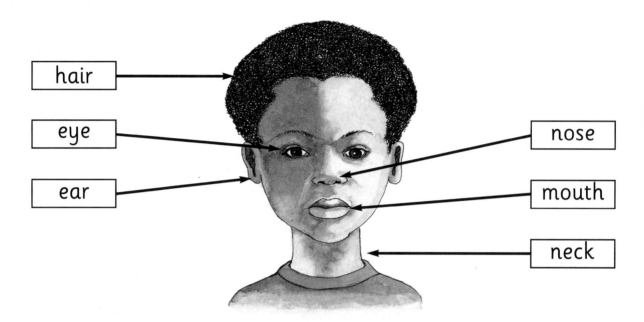

hair

eye

ear

nose

mouth

neck

All these words are **parts of the head**.

Practice

Copy the sentences. Choose the correct word to fill the gap.

1. I smell with my _____nose_____ .

2. I hear with my _____ .

3. I see with my _____ .

4. I eat with my _____ .

5. On top of my head I have _____ .

6. My head is joined to my body by my _____ .

More to think about

Find the hidden words. They all name parts of the body.
Make a list.

1. acb**arm**degh

2. lkjhandipkm

3. zchestvdqwk

4. vcxzakneeo

5. footdsawyug

6. hjfanklewer

7. zshoulderxh

8. jklelbowmb

9. qwertylegac

10. wristyuoph

Now try these

Name the part of the body.

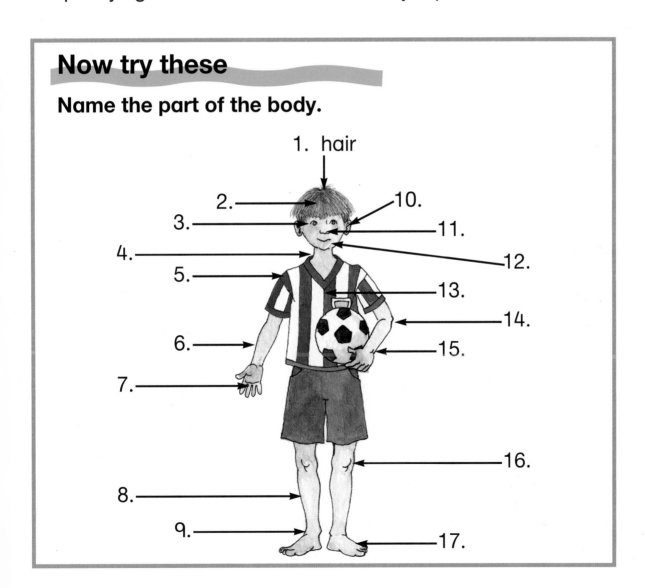

1. hair
2.
3.
4.
5.
6.
7.
8.
9.
10.
11.
12.
13.
14.
15.
16.
17.

UNIT 3 ar

Listen to the **sound** made by the letters **ar**.

car

bark

Practice

Add ar. Write the word that matches the picture.

p _____ k   c _____ d   d _____ k

d _____ t   sh _____ k   st _____

1.   2.    3.

4.    5.   6.

More to think about

Copy the table. Write the words in the correct columns.

ar	art
jar	

Now try these

1. Copy the sentences. Choose the correct word.
   a) A (star/start) shines in the sky.
   b) A (dart/spark) flew out of the fire.
   c) John plays football in the (park/part).
   d) Shirin ate all the (tart/tar) on her plate.

2. Make up a sentence for each word.
   a) farm   b) mark   c) start

4 Adding ing and ed

The letters **ing** or **ed** can be added to many words.

Abena is kick**ing** the ball.

When **ing** is added to a word it often means it is **happening now**.

Jason kick**ed** the ball.

When **ed** is added to a word it means it has **already happened**.

Practice

Copy the words.
Circle the ing endings. Underline the ed endings.

a) sing(ing)   b) pull<u>ed</u>   c) holding   d) falling

e) opened   f) lasted   g) sleeping   h) locked

More to think about

Copy and complete the table.

	+ ing	+ ed
roll	rolling	rolled
look		
jump		
play		
help		
comb		
call		
open		

Now try these

1. Copy the sentences. Choose the word with the correct ending.
   a) Tim (jumping/jumped) in the puddle and got wet.
   b) Pen is (looking/looked) for her dog.
   c) Dawn is (helping/helped) her dad in the kitchen.
   d) Tuhil (rolling/rolled) the snow into a ball.
   e) Jo (opening/opened) the box and out popped the surprise!

2. Make up a sentence for each word.
   a) playing   b) combed   c) pulled

oi and oy

The letters **oi** and **oy** often make the same sound.

b**oi**l

b**oy**

The **oi** sound is often found in the **middle** of words.

The **oy** sound is often found at the **end** of short words.

Practice

Write the word that matches the picture.

boy	toy	soil	coin

1.

2.

3.

4.

More to think about

Copy the sentences. Choose a word from the box to fill the gap.

boy	joy	toy	soil	coin	boil	point

1. The baby was playing with a _____.

2. A penny is a _____.

3. Ben was a small _____.

4. When you are happy, you jump with _____.

5. Plants grow in _____.

6. Dad put the kettle on to _____.

7. It is rude to _____.

Now try these

1. Copy the table. Write the words in the box in the correct columns.

join	enjoy	annoy	moist	noise	avoid	joy

oy words	**oi** words
	join

2. Make up three sentences.
   Use an **oy** or **oi** word in each sentence.

Vowels and consonants

Look at the alphabet **letters**.
There are five **vowels**: a e i o u.

a b c d e f g h i j k l m n o p q r s t u v w x y z

All the other letters are **consonants**.

All words have a **vowel** or the letter **y** in them.

Practice

Copy the words. Underline the vowel in each word.

1. hut

2. tap

3. cat

4. mill

5. frog

6. pen

More to think about

Copy the words. Fill in the missing vowels.

sun

j__t

b__s

b__t

m__n

c__t

p__nd

d__ck

b__n

Now try these

1. Copy the table. Write the words in the box in the correct columns.

| boy tap van bat tin fish bug man |
| hat bun rat sun ball pen |

words with a	words with e	words with i	words with o	words with u
			boy	

2. Write two more words in each column.

ow and ou

The letters **ow** and **ou** often make the same **sound**.

cl**ow**n

cl**ou**d

Practice

Write the word that matches the picture.

| cow | house | crown | mouth |

1.

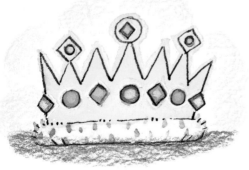

2.

3.

4.

More to think about

Write the sentences. Choose a word from the box to fill each gap.

owl	shouted	town	pound	down	sound

1. The window cleaner climbed _____ the ladder.

2. The _____ hooted as he flew about that night.

3. Mum took Meera to _____ to buy some shoes.

4. Richard paid a _____ for his ticket.

5. The harp made a beautiful _____ .

6. The children _____ to their friends who were a long way away.

Now try these

1. Copy the table. Write the words in the box in the correct columns.

howl	found	scout	now	out
mouse		brown	down	

ow words	**ou** words
howl	

2. Make up three sentences. Use an **ow** or **ou** word in each sentence.

17

Antonyms

Antonyms are words with **opposite meanings**.

dry   **wet**

These words are **antonyms**.

Practice

Copy the word lists. Match each word with its antonym.

old	long
clean	poor
short	young
fat	shut
rich	dull
shiny	thin
open	dark
light	dirty

More to think about

Find the hidden antonyms.

1. dry   ab**wet**cde

2. quick   fslowghij

3. small   bigklmnop

4. cold   qrstuhotv

5. happy   wxsadyzab

6. soft   gkhardmn

Now try these

Copy the sentences. Write an antonym for the underlined word in the gap.

1. Tara is not <u>weak</u>. She is ___strong___ .

2. Ben is not <u>awake</u>. He is _____ .

3. I <u>love</u> ice cream but I _____ cabbage.

4. The scissors are <u>blunt</u> and we need _____ ones.

5. My glass is <u>empty</u> but your glass is _____ .

6. Grandma is an <u>old</u> lady. Sue is a _____ girl.

UNIT 9

air and ear

The letters **air** and **ear** often make the same **sound**.

fair

b**ear**

Practice

Copy the words. Underline the letters that make the same sound as air in fair.

1.

st<u>air</u>

2.

hair

3.
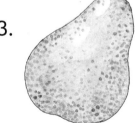

pear

4.

fair

5.

tear

6.

bear

More to think about

Copy the table. Write the words in the correct columns.

air	ear
hair	

fair

hair

pear

stair

chair

bear

Now try these

1. Write the sentences. Choose the correct word.
   a) The old lady put on her new (stair/pair) of shoes.
   b) Matthew loved going to the (fair/airport) to watch the planes.
   c) Sam was scared of the (chair/bear).
   d) The princess had to (wear/pear) a long red dress.

2. Make up a sentence for each of these words.
   a) pear   b) air   c) hair

Compound words

A **compound word** is two small words joined together.

snow + ball
= snowball

Practice

Join the small words together. Write the compound word.

1. snow + man = <u>snowman</u>

2. hand + bag = _____

3. tea + spoon = _____

4. sun + light = _____

5. foot + ball = _____

6. air + port = _____

More to think about

Write the compound word. Then write its two short words.

1. rainbow = ____rain____ + ____bow____

2. handbag = _____ + _____

3. afternoon = _____ + _____

4. everything = _____ + _____

5. lunchtime = _____ + _____

6. someone = _____ + _____

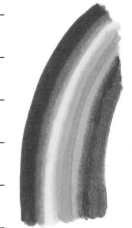

Now try these

1. Write the compound word.

a) + = ____raindrop____

b) + = _____

c) + = _____

d) + = _____

2. Write a sentence for each compound word.

Progress Test A

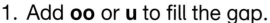

1. Add **oo** or **u** to fill the gap.

   a)

   b)

   c)

   d)

   b ____ k   b ____ ll   c ____ k   p ____ lley

2. Write a part of the body that begins with the letter.

   a) a _____   b) e _____   c) f _____   d) h _____

3. Write the sentences. Choose the correct word.

   a) It is (dart/dark) at night.

   b) Stella got a birthday (card/cart) from her gran.

   c) Peta travelled to the party in a (bar/car).

4. Copy and complete the table.

	+ ing	+ ed
jump		
call		
help		
pull		
scream		

5. Choose **oy** or **oi** to complete each word.

   a) s ____ l   b) t ____   c) c ____ n   d) b ____

6. Write the names of five friends. Circle the vowels in each name.

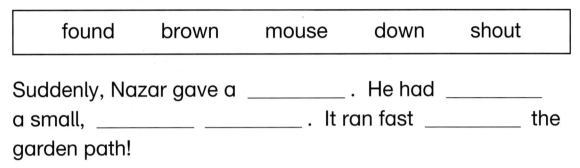

7. Copy the sentences. Choose a word from the box to fill each gap.

found	brown	mouse	down	shout

Suddenly, Nazar gave a _____ . He had _____ a small, _____ _____ . It ran fast _____ the garden path!

8. Match each word in Box A with its antonym in Box B.

Box A	hot fast small bad long sad hard

Box B	short big good cold slow soft happy

9. Write the words. Underline the letters that make the same sound as **air** in **fair**.
   a) hair   b) bear   c) stair   d) pear
   e) pair   f) wear   g) chair   h) airport

10. Choose a word from the box to complete the compound word.

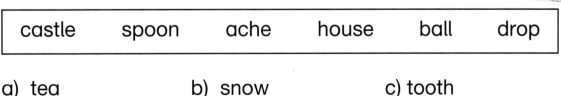

castle	spoon	ache	house	ball	drop

   a) tea   b) snow   c) tooth
   d) green   e) rain   f) sand

UNIT 11 — or and aw

The letters **or** and **aw** often make a similar **sound**.

horse

claw

Practice

Write the words. Underline the letters that make the same sound as **or** in short.

1.

torch

2.

lawn

3.

storm

4.

fork

5.

stork

6.

paw

More to think about

Copy the table. Write the words in the correct columns.

aw	or
	horn

corn

lawn   horn

fort

yawn   cord

crawl

paw

Now try these

1. Copy the sentences. Choose the correct word.
   a) Kelly's (torch/horn) lit up the dark room.
   b) The children had to (draw/claw) pictures
      of their stories.
   c) Aman rode his (stork/horse) every morning.
   d) The baby had just started to (paw/crawl).

2. Make up a sentence for each word.
   a) paw   b) storm   c) horn

All these **words** can be used to write **a story**.

Practice

Match the beginning of the sentence to its ending. Copy the sentence.

1. The giant was   magic spells.

2. A princess lived   in the woods.

3. The prince rode   waved her wand.

4. The magician made   very big.

5. The little fairy   a white horse.

6. The dragon played   in the castle.

More to think about

Write the words that match the picture.

a good fairy	a dark cave	a black cat
a fat frog	a beautiful princess	an ugly troll
a tall tower	a thatched cottage	a cunning fox

1.

2.

3.

4.

5.

6.

7.

8.

9.

Now try these

Copy the table. Write the words in the correct columns.

| pirate   castle   fox   woodcutter   giant   lion   forest |
| lake   queen   wolf   unicorn   mountain |

people	animals	places

er, ir and ur

The letters **er**, **ir** and **ur** often make a similar **sound**.

k**er**b

b**ir**d

f**ur**

Practice

Write the words. Underline the letters that make the same sound as ir in bird.

1.

fur

2.

herd

3.

skirt

4.

flower

5.

girl

6.

nurse

More to think about

Copy the table. Write the words in the correct columns.

ir	ur	er
		flower

bird

purse

fir

church

flower

herd

shirt

fern

churn

Now try these

1. Copy the sentences. Choose the correct word.
   a) Andy put (letter/butter) and jam on his bread.
   b) The (bird/skirt) sang as it sat in the tree.
   c) Clare took money from her (fur/purse) to pay.
   d) Jack slipped off the (kerb/herb)when crossing
      the road.

2. Make up a sentence for each word.
   a) flower   b) stir   c) hurt

Syllables

Each beat in a word is a **syllable**.

Say the word **dinosaur**.
Count the **beats** as you say the word.

di—no—saur

The word **dinosaur** has three **syllables**.

Practice

Copy the words. Write the missing syllables.

1. pencil   =   pen –

2. picture   =   pic –

3. potato   =   po – ta –

4. pasta   =   pas –

5. computer =   com – pu –

More to think about

Write the syllables for these words.

1. melon   =   me – lon

2. present   =

3. bat   =

4. magnet   =

5. sisters   =

Now try these

1. Copy the words. Write the number of syllables in each word.

a)

    sausage (2)

b)

    garden

c)

    cat

d)

    hippopotamus

e)

    cucumber

f)

    message

2. Copy the table. Write two words in each column.

1-syllable words	**2-syllable** words	**3-syllable** words

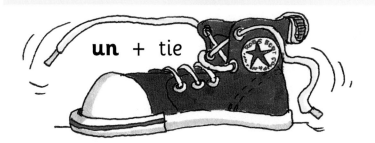

UNIT 15 Prefixes

A **prefix** is a group of letters added to the **beginning** of a word.

un and **dis** are **prefixes**.

un + tie

dis + appear

When **un** or **dis** is added to a word, the meaning of the word changes to its **antonym** (**opposite meaning**).

Practice

Copy these words. Underline each prefix.

1. unlock

2. dislike

3. disagree

4. unlucky

More to think about

Add the prefix to the word.

1. equal = unequal

2. un + tie =

3. born =

4. trust =

5. dis + obey =

6. like =

Now try these

1. Copy the sentences. Choose a word from the box to fill each gap.

uneven	dislike	unhappy	disobey

a) If you don't like something, you _____ it.

b) The children were not happy, they were _____.

c) The path was not even, it was _____.

d) If you don't obey a rule, you _____ it.

2. Write four more words with the prefixes **un** and **dis**.

wh and ph

Listen to the **sounds** made by the letters **wh** and **ph**.

whale

ele**ph**ant

Practice

Copy the words. Underline the wh and ph sounds.

1.

whistle

2.

dolphin

3.

photograph

4.

alphabet

5.

whisk

6.

wheel

More to think about

Copy the sentences. Answer the questions using the correct word from the box.

elephant	whisker	photograph	wheel	dolphin	white

What do you think I am?

1. I have a rubber tyre around me. _____

2. I swim in the sea. _____

3. I am taken with a camera. _____

4. I stick out from a cat's face. _____

5. I am the colour of snow. _____

6. I am a big, strong animal. _____

Now try these

1. Copy the table. List all the **wh** and **ph** words on pages 36 and 37. Write the words in the correct columns.

wh	ph
whale	

2. Write three more words in each column. Use a dictionary to help you.

Collecting words (3)

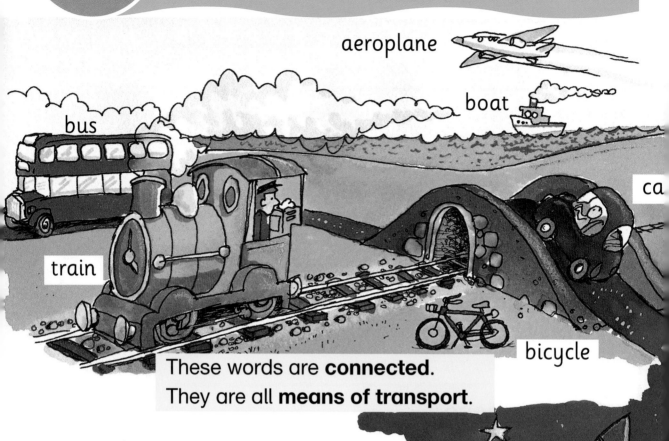

aeroplane

boat

bus

ca

train

bicycle

These words are **connected**.
They are all **means of transport**.

Practice

Copy the sentences. Choose the correct word to complete each sentence.

1. A (car/boat) has four wheels.

2. An (ship/aeroplane) flies in the sky.

3. A (boat/bike) floats on water.

4. A (tractor/bus) carries a lot of people.

5. A (rocket/coach) zooms into space.

6. A farmer rides a (rocket/tractor).

More to think about

Copy the table. Write the words in the box in the correct columns.

| bus | aeroplane | boat | train | helicopter | bicycle |
| lorry | glider | rocket | raft | yacht | submarine |

land transport	**sea** transport	**air** transport

Now try these

1. Copy the words. Circle the first letter of each word.
   Write the words in alphabetical order.

   coach   ambulance   dinghy   barge

2. Write these words in alphabetical order.

   motorcycle   jet   lorry   kayak

Suffixes

A **suffix** is a group of letters added to the **end** of a word.

help**ful**

Jim was help**ful**
in the garden.

lone**ly**

Sonia is lone**ly**
on her own.

The letters **ful** and **ly** are **suffixes**.

Practice

Add the suffix. Write the word.

1. pain   +   ful   =   _____painful_____

2. safe   +   ly   =   _____

3. care   +   ful   =   _____

4. love   +   ly   =   _____

5. wonder   +   ful   =   _____

More to think about

Copy the table. Write the words in the box in the correct columns.

careful	safely	lonely	painful	smartly	helpful

ly	ful

Now try these

1. Copy the sentences. Fill each gap with a word from the box.

lovely	painful	smartly	careful

   a) Mei Mei looked _____ in her new dress.

   b) Tariq was _____ not to trip as he ran down the path.

   c) Emma and Grant were dressed _____ for the wedding.

   d) When Ben bumped his head it was very _____.

2. Make up a sentence for each of these words.
   a) useful   b) lonely   c) safely

Listen to the **different sounds** made by the letters **ea**.

h**ea**d

sp**ear**

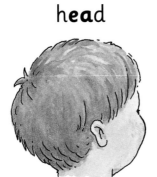

Practice

Copy the table. Match the words in the box with the
ea sound in the columns

bread	hear	tread	fear	beard	tear
	thread	team	spread		

ea as in h**ea**d	ea as in sp**ear**

More to think about

Match a word in the box with a picture.
Write the rhyming word.

bread	tear	feather	spear	scream	head

1. **spread**   rhymes with   <u> bread </u>

2. **gear**   rhymes with   _____

3. **weather**   rhymes with   _____

4. **year**   rhymes with   _____

5. **team**   rhymes with   _____

6. **dead**   rhymes with   _____

Now try these

Fill in the missing letters. Each word contains an ea sound.

1. Water flows in this.   s __ __ __ __ __

2. You eat this with jam.   b __ __ __ __

3. You feel this when you are afraid.   f __ __ __

4. You need this for sewing.   t __ __ __ __ __

5. A new one starts on the 1st January. y __ __ __

Synonyms

Synonyms are words with **similar** meanings.

Tom was **happy** on his birthday. He felt **cheerful**.

The words **happy** and **cheerful** are **synonyms**.

Practice

Write a synonym from the box for each word.

big	small	start	wet	quick	difficult

1. tiny <u>small</u>

2. fast _____

3. begin _____

4. huge _____

5. hard _____

6. damp _____

More to think about

Copy the lists. Underline the synonym for the first word in each list.

1. scared   hot   <u>frightened</u>   trees

2. finish   cat   book   end

3. sick   ill   grass   wet

4. happy   clever   low   joyful

5. foolish   day   silly   empty

6. sad   went   mop   unhappy

Now try these

Copy the pairs of sentences. Choose a synonym from the box to complete the second sentence in each pair.

dropped	thirsty	soon	cold	deaf

1. We will go out to play in a short while.
   We will go out to play _____ .

2. Shireen let the cup fall on the floor.
   Shireen _____ the cup on the floor.

3. The old lady cannot hear.
   The old lady is _____ .

4. The dog was in need of a drink.
   The dog was _____ .

5. The water was very chilly.
   The water was very _____ .

Progress Test B

1. Copy the words. Underline the letters that make the same sound as **aw** in cl**aw**.
   a) lawn b) short c) saw
   d) horn e) sport f) fawn

2. Write the beginning of each sentence with its correct ending.

   a) A brown bear   chased a mouse.

   b) The black cat   jumped in the pond.

   c) The beautiful princess makes wishes come true.

   d) Two fat frogs   lived in the big cave.

   e) A good fairy   slept in the castle.

3. Copy the table. Write three words in each column.

ir 	ur	er

46

4. Split these words into syllables. Write the syllables.
   a) tractor
   b) rocket
   c) sausage
   d) cat
   e) elephant
   f) alphabet
   g) animal
   h) book
   i) cucumber

5. Copy and complete these words with the prefix **un** or **dis**.

   a) _____ tie
   b) _____ born
   c) _____ trust

   d) _____ happy
   e) _____ obey
   f) _____ lucky

6. Copy the table. Write the words in the box in the correct columns.

elephant   whisper   dolphin   photograph   whale whistle   telephone   wheel   alphabet

ph	wh

7. Write two types of transport for each group.

   a) Transport by **land**

   b) Transport by **sea**

   c) Transport by **air**

8. Copy the sentences. Fill each gap with a word from the box.

lonely	careful	useful	safely

a) Be _____ when you cross the road.

b) Laith used the zebra crossing to cross the busy road _____.

c) Rory felt _____ walking around the zoo on his own.

d) Jo thought her colouring pens were very _____.

9. Write the word that rhymes.

a) **fear** rhymes with _____

b) **weather** rhymes with _____

c) **cream** rhymes with _____

d) **bread** rhymes with _____

e) **year** rhymes with _____

10. Write a synonym for each word.

a) big   b) sad   c) cry

d) shout   e) fall   f) start

g) fast   h) tiny   i) lumpy